COLLECTIONS
FOR YOUNG SCHOLARS™

VOLUME I BOOK I

Games

Folk Tales

Art by Robert Byrd

COLLECTIONS FOR YOUNG SCHOLARS™

VOLUME I BOOK I

PROGRAM AUTHORS
Marilyn Jager Adams
Carl Bereiter
Jan Hirshberg
Valerie Anderson
S. A. Bernier

CONSULTING AUTHORS
Michael Pressley
Iva Carruthers
Bill Pinkney

OPEN COURT PUBLISHING COMPANY
CHICAGO AND PERU, ILLINOIS

CHAIRMAN
M. Blouke Carus

PRESIDENT
André W. Carus

EDUCATION DIRECTOR
Carl Bereiter

CONCEPT
Barbara Conteh

EXECUTIVE EDITORS
Nancy Dyer
Shirley Graudin

SENIOR PROJECT EDITORS
Linda Cave
Nancy Johnson

ART DIRECTOR
John Grandits

VICE-PRESIDENT, PRODUCTION AND
MANUFACTURING
Chris Vancalbergh

PERMISSIONS COORDINATOR
Diane Sikora

COVER ARTIST
Robert Byrd

ॐ 4

OPEN COURT and ✳ are registered trademarks of Open Court Publishing Company.

COLLECTIONS FOR YOUNG SCHOLARS is a trademark of Open Court Publishing Company.

Copyright © 1995 Open Court Publishing Company

All rights reserved for all countries. No part of this work may be reproduced or utilized in any form or by any means, electronic or mechanical, including photocopying, recording, or by any information storage or retrieval system, without the written permission of Open Court Publishing Company unless such copying is expressly permitted by federal copyright law. Address requests for permission to reproduce Open Court material to Permissions Coordinator, Open Court Publishing Company, 315 Fifth Street, Peru IL 61354.

Printed in the United States of America

ISBN 0-8126-1148-9

10 9 8 7 6 5 4 3

ACKNOWLEDGMENTS

Grateful acknowledgment is given to the following publishers and copyright owners for permission granted to reprint selections from their publications. All possible care has been taken to trace ownership and secure permission for each selection included.

Carolrhoda Books, Inc., Minneapolis, MN: *Jafta* by Hugh Lewin, illustrated by Lisa Kopper, text copyright © 1981 by Hugh Lewin, illustrations copyright © 1981 by Lisa Kopper.

Dutton Children's Books, a division of Penguin Books USA Inc.: *Matthew and Tilly* by Rebecca C. Jones, illustrated by Beth Peck, text copyright © 1991 by Rebecca C. Jones, illustrations copyright © 1991 by Beth Peck.

HarperCollins Publishers: An excerpt entitled "A Game Called Piggle" from *Piggle* by Crosby Bonsall, copyright © 1973 by Crosby Bonsall. "The Big Team Relay Race" from *On Your Mark, Get Set, Go! The First All-Animal Olympics* by Leonard Kessler, copyright © 1972 by Leonard Kessler.

Edizioni E. Elle, Trieste, Italy: "Little Green Riding Hood" from *Telephone Tales* by Gianni Rodari, © Edizioni E. Elle.

Holiday House: *Anansi and the Talking Melon* by Eric A. Kimmel, illustrated by Janet Stevens, text copyright © 1994 by Eric A. Kimmel, illustrations copyright © 1994 by Janet Stevens.

GAMES

❧

FOLK TALES

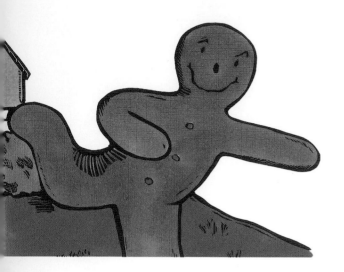

A GAME CALLED PIGGLE

from PIGGLE by Crosby Bonsall

"Oh, Bear," Homer said,
"will you play a game with me?"
Bear said, "Yes, I will.
What shall we play?"

🌱 12

13 ❧

"Do you know a game called Piggle?"
Homer asked.

"Piggle . . . Piggle," Bear said.
"Piggle like triggle, hmmmm."

"Triggle, Bear?" Homer said.

"Triggle," Bear said.

"Triggle like biggle."

"Oh," said Homer.

"Let me think," said Bear.

"Piggle like miggle."

"Miggle, Bear?" Homer said.

"Miggle like diggle," Bear said.

"Oh," said Homer.

"Give me time," said Bear.
"Let me see now,
we have triggle and biggle,
miggle and diggle like Piggle."

"Oh, *I* see," cried Homer.

"Let me try.

Wiggle, giggle,

sniggle and figgle like Piggle.

That's *it*, Bear. I can play!"

"Yes, you can," cried Bear.
"Maybe I know the game of Piggle
after all. It sounds nice."

"Yes, it does," Homer said.
"Let's piggle some more.
Ishy, wishy, fishy, dishy."

Bear sang, "Diddley, widdley,
fiddley, riddley."

And together they sang,
"Mumpity, wumpity,
dumpity, lumpity."

JAFTA
A Shared Reading Story
Hugh Lewin
illustrated by Lisa Kopper

When I'm happy, said Jafta, I purr like a lioncub,

or skip like a spider,

or laugh like a hyena.

And sometimes I want to jump like an impala,

and dance like a zebra,

or just nuzzle like a rabbit.

When I get tired, I like lazing in the sun like a lizard,
  or wallowing warm like a hippo,
  and feeling cuddly like a lamb.

9 24   But when I get cross, I stamp like an elephant
and grumble like a warthog.

(I don't often get cross, said Jafta.)

And I can be as strong as a rhino.

Sometimes I want to be as tall as a giraffe,

as long as a snake.

And I want to run as fast as a cheetah,
as quick as an ostrich,

or swing through the trees like a monkey,
and fly high high high like an eagle,

or just stand very still, like a crane on one leg.

But actually, said Jafta,

I don't think there's anything quite so nice

27 ❧

as being a flamingo flying off into the sunset . . .

THE BIG TEAM RELAY RACE

from ON YOUR MARK, GET SET, GO!
by Leonard Kessler
illustrated by Linda Kelen

The animals are playing games. The teams are
the Yankees, the Tigers, and the Pirates. Worm wants
to play, but she is not on a team.

"All teams line up
for the big team relay race," Owl said.
Dog, Frog, and Turtle went
to the starting line. Duck, Rabbit, and Cat
waited down the track. Frog and Turtle
each had a little stick.

"Where is my stick?" asked Dog.

"Who has the stick?" asked Owl.

"Get a stick. I need a stick!" yelled Dog.

Worm wiggled over to Owl.

"I am ready, Coach," said Worm.

"Hey, Worm," said Owl.

"You can be Dog's stick!"

"Wow! I am on a team!" said Worm.

"I'm a Yankee!"

"Okay," said Owl. "Each of you
must run with your stick. Then pass it on
to your other team member. And remember,"
said Owl, "the stick must cross the finish line."

"Okay," said little Bird.

"ON YOUR MARK, GET SET, GO!"

31

Zoom! Down the track they ran.
Cat, Rabbit, and Duck were waiting.
"Here they come," yelled Duck.

Turtle gave his stick to Cat.

Frog gave his stick to Rabbit.

And Dog gave his stick to Duck.

Zoom! Cat, Rabbit, and Duck ran down the track.

33

"Duck is winning, Duck is winning!" yelled Dog.

Duck smiled and waved to the cheering crowd.

34

She tripped over her big web feet

and fell into a big mud puddle. Squoosh!

"Get up, Duck," shouted Dog.

"Yikes," yelled Duck, "I am stuck in the mud!"

"Don't worry, Duck," said Worm.

"I will win the race for our team."

Worm wiggled and wiggled.

She wiggled past the finish line—first!

"WORM IS THE WINNER!" yelled Spider.

"The Yankees win!" shouted Dog.

"Let's give a cheer for Worm," yelled Owl.

"Squiggle squiggle,
Who can wiggle?
Wiggle wiggle
Wiggle Worm.
Yay, yay, Worm!"

37

MARY MACK

illustrated by Bob Barner

Oh, Mary Mack, Mack, Mack,

All dressed in black, black, black,

With silver buttons, buttons, buttons,

All down her back, back, back.

She asked her mother, mother, mother,

For fifty cents, cents, cents,

To watch the elephant, elephant, elephant,

Jump over the fence, fence, fence.

He jumped so high, high, high,

That he reached the sky, sky, sky,

And he didn't come back, back, back,

'Til the Fourth of July, 'ly, 'ly.

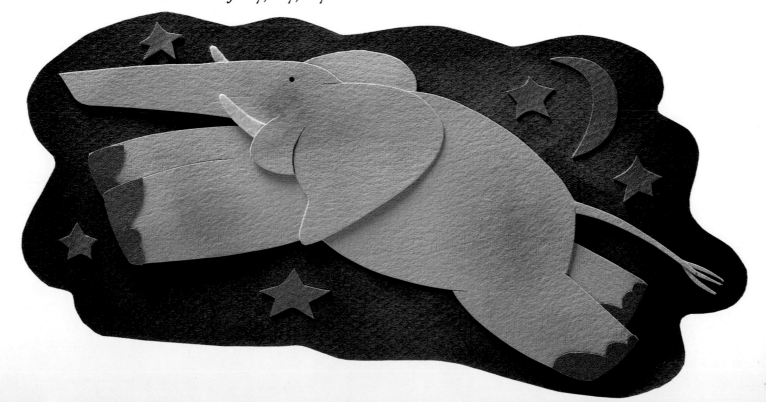

"Soap Box Racing". c. 1939–1940. William H. Johnson.

Tempera, pen, and ink on paper, 14 1/8" x 17 7/8". Gift of the Harmon Foundation, National Museum of American Art,
Smithsonian Institution. 1967.59.160. © Smithsonian Institution. Photo: Art Resource, New York

Children playing games.
Date unknown.

Marble high relief on a child's sarcophagus. Kunsthistorisches
Museum, Vienna. Photo: © Erich Lessing/Art Resource

FINE ART
GAMES

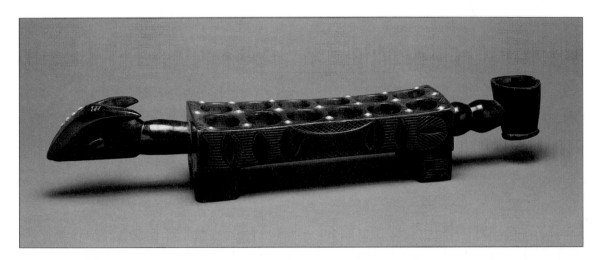

Game board.
20th century. Dan people,
Liberia/Ivory Coast.

Wood and metal. Gift of Katherine White and
the Boeing Company, Seattle Art Museum.
81.17.205. Photo: Susan Dirk

41 ❧

Ballplay of the Sioux on the St. Peters River in Winter. 1848. Seth Eastman.

Oil on canvas. Acquisition in memory of Mitchell A. Wilder, Director, Amon Carter Museum, 1961–1979. Amon Carter Museum, Fort Worth, Texas. 1979.4

MATTHEW AND TILLY

Rebecca C. Jones

illustrated by Beth Peck

Matthew and Tilly were friends.

They rode bikes together,

and they played hide-and-seek together.

They sold lemonade together.

When business was slow,

they played sidewalk games together.

And sometimes they ate ice-cream cones together.

Once they even rescued a lady's kitten

from a tree together.

The lady gave them money
for the bubble-gum machines.

So later they chewed gum together
and remembered how brave they had been.

Sometimes, though, Matthew and Tilly
got sick of each other.

One day when they were coloring,
Matthew broke Tilly's purple crayon.
He didn't mean to, but he did.
"You broke my crayon,"
Tilly said in her crabbiest voice.
"It was an old crayon,"
Matthew said in his grouchiest voice.
"It was ready to break."

"No, it wasn't," Tilly said.

"It was a brand-new crayon, and you broke it.

You always break everything."

"Stop being so picky," Matthew said.

"You're always so picky

and stinky and mean."

"Well, you're so stupid," Tilly said.

"You're so stupid

and stinky and mean."

Matthew stomped up the stairs. By himself.

Tilly found a piece of chalk
and began drawing numbers and squares
on the sidewalk. By herself.

Upstairs, Matthew got out
his cash register
and some cans
so he could play store.
He piled the cans
extra high,
and he put prices
on everything.

This was the best store
he had ever made.
Probably because that picky
and stinky and mean old Tilly
wasn't around to mess it up.
But he didn't have a customer.
And playing store wasn't much fun
without a customer.

Tilly finished drawing the numbers and squares.

She drew them really big,

with lots of squiggly lines.

This was the best sidewalk game

she had ever drawn.

Probably because that stupid

and stinky and mean old Matthew

wasn't around to mess it up.

But she didn't have anyone to play with.

And a sidewalk game wasn't much fun

without another player.

Matthew looked out the window
and wondered what Tilly was doing.
Tilly looked up at Matthew's window
and wondered what he was doing.
She smiled, just a little.
That was enough for Matthew.
"I'm sorry," he called.
"So am I," said Tilly.

And Matthew ran downstairs so they could play.

Together again.

BIBLIOGRAPHY

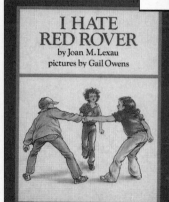

Hooray for Snail!

by John Stadler

Snail hits the ball to the moon. Will he make it around the bases before the ball gets back?

I Hate Red Rover

by Joan M. Lexau

Jill hates recess until her grandfather helps her learn to play.

Morris and Boris: Three Stories

by Bernard Wiseman

Boris wants to teach Morris to play games, but the silly moose just can't do anything right.

Piggle

by Crosby Bonsall

Read more about Homer, his friends, and the game of Piggle.

56

Pigs in Hiding

by Arlene Dubanevich

Ninety-nine silly pigs hide in a game of hide-and-seek.

Play Ball, Zachary!

by Muriel Blaustein

Zachary the tiger cub is a real fumblepaws when he plays ball.

Ronald Morgan Goes to Bat

by Patricia Reilly Giff

Ronald can't hit and he can't catch, but his team needs him just the same.

The Worst Team Ever

by Leonard Kessler

The Greenhoppers are the worst swampball players in the world.

FOLK TALES

THE GINGERBREAD MAN

retold by Jo Olson

illustrated by Nelle Davis

Once upon a time,
a little old man and a little old woman
lived all alone in a little old house.

"I wish we had a child," said the man.

"I will make one out of gingerbread," said the woman.

So she made a gingerbread man and popped him
into the oven to bake.

Soon the gingerbread man was done.

The little old man opened the oven to peek inside.

Out hopped the gingerbread man—and away he ran.

"Stop!" cried the little old man.

But the gingerbread man ran down the road.

He looked back and sang,

"Run, run as fast as you can.

You can't catch me.

I'm the gingerbread man!"

The man and the woman ran as fast as they could.

But they couldn't catch him.

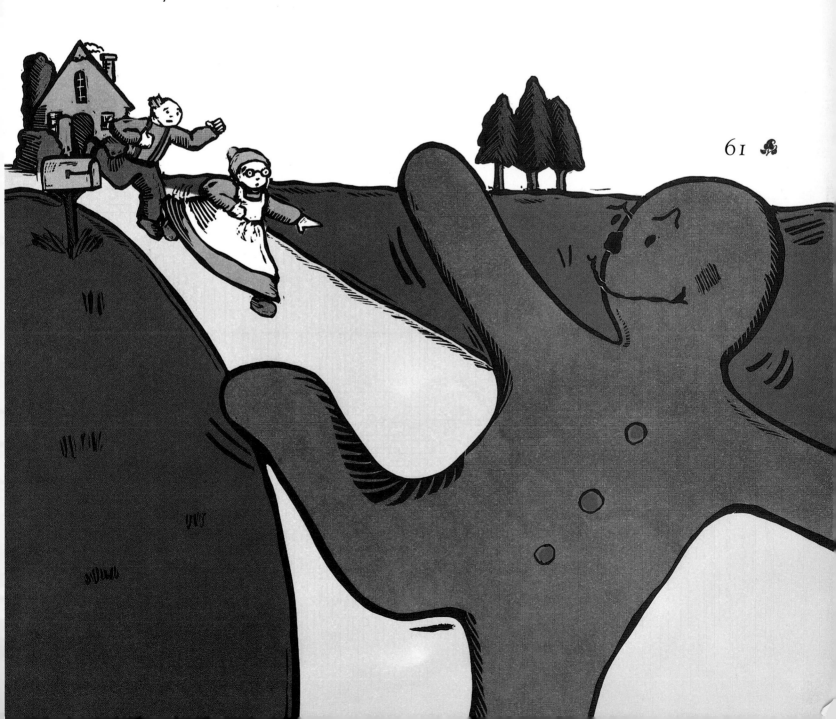

61

Soon the gingerbread man saw a cow.

"Stop!" said the cow. "You look good to eat."

"No," said the gingerbread man.

"I have run away from a man and a woman.

I will run away from you, too."

The cow ran after the gingerbread man.

He sang,

"Run, run as fast as you can.

You can't catch me.

I'm the gingerbread man!"

And the cow couldn't catch him.

Soon the gingerbread man saw a horse.

"Stop!" said the horse. "You look good to eat."

"No," said the gingerbread man.
"I have run away from a man and a woman
and a cow. I will run away from you, too."

The horse ran after the gingerbread man.
He sang,

"Run, run as fast as you can.

You can't catch me.

I'm the gingerbread man!"

And the horse couldn't catch him.

63

Soon the gingerbread man saw
some workers raking hay.
"Stop!" said the workers.
"You look good to eat."
    "No," said the gingerbread man.
"I have run away from a man and
a woman and a cow and a horse.
I will run away from you, too."

The workers ran after the gingerbread man.

He sang,

"Run, run as fast as you can.

You can't catch me.

I'm the gingerbread man!"

And the workers couldn't catch him.

65

Soon the gingerbread man saw a fox

sitting by the edge of the river.

"I'm not afraid of you,"

the gingerbread man said to the fox.

"I have run away from a man and a woman

and a cow and a horse and some workers.

I can run away from you, too."

"I don't want to catch you,"
said the fox. "I will help you run away.
Jump on my back. I will take you
across the river."

So the gingerbread man hopped up
on the fox's back. The fox began to swim.

"It's too wet on my back," said the fox.
"Jump on my nose. I will hold you
out of the water."

The gingerbread man jumped
on the fox's nose. The fox opened his mouth.
Snip, snap, gulp!
That was the end of the gingerbread man.

69

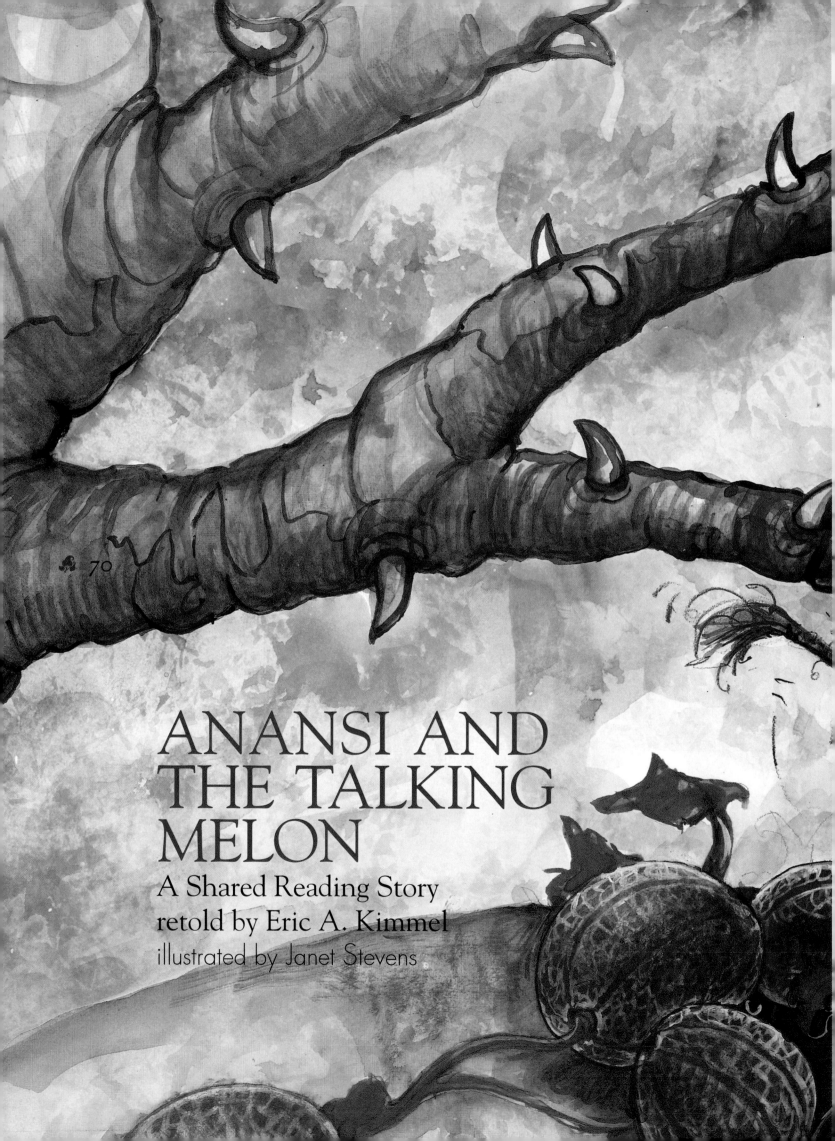

ANANSI AND THE TALKING MELON

A Shared Reading Story
retold by Eric A. Kimmel
illustrated by Janet Stevens

One fine morning Anansi the Spider
sat high up in a thorn tree
looking down into Elephant's garden.
Elephant was hoeing his melon patch.
The ripe melons seemed to call out to Anansi,
"Look how juicy and sweet we are!
Come eat us!"

71

Anansi loved to eat melons,

but he was much too lazy to grow them himself.

So he sat up in the thorn tree, watching and waiting,

while the sun rose high in the sky and the day grew warm.

By the time noon came, it was too hot to work.

Elephant put down his hoe

and went inside his house to take a nap.

Here was the moment Anansi had been waiting for.

He broke off a thorn and dropped down into the melon patch.

He used the thorn to bore a hole

in the biggest, ripest melon.

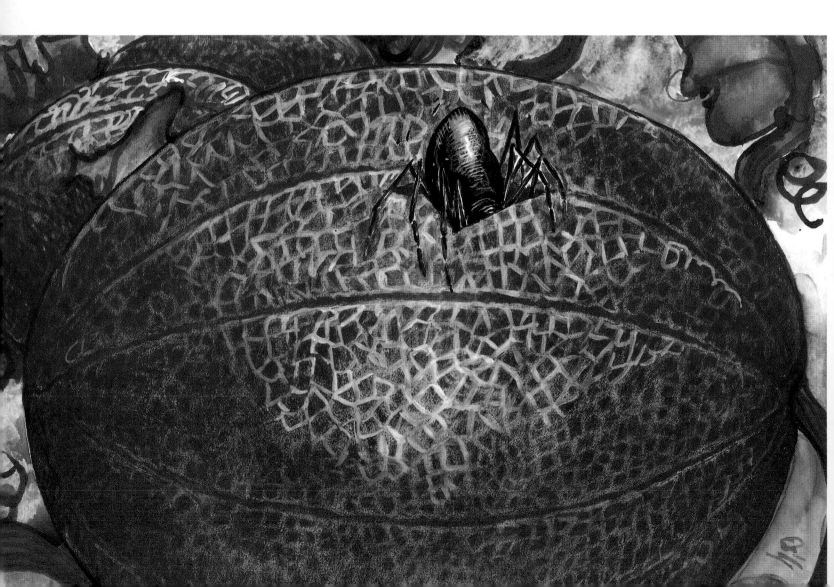

Anansi squeezed inside
and started eating. He ate and ate
until he was as round as a berry.

"I'm full," Anansi said at last.
"Elephant will be coming back soon.
It is time to go."

But when he tried
to squeeze through the hole,
Anansi had a surprise.
He didn't fit!
The hole was big enough
for a thin spider,
but much too small
for a fat one.

73 🕷

"I'm stuck!" Anansi cried. "I can't get out.
I will have to wait until I am thin again."

Anansi sat down on a pile of melon seeds
and waited to get thin.
Time passed slowly.

"I'm bored," Anansi said.
"I wish I had something to do."

Just then he heard Elephant returning to the garden.
Anansi had an idea. "When Elephant gets closer,
I will say something. Elephant will think
the melon is talking. What fun!"

Elephant walked over to the melon patch.
"Look at this fine melon. How big and ripe it is!"
he said, picking it up.

"Ouch!" cried Anansi.

Elephant jumped.

"Aah! Who said that?"

"I did. The melon,"
Anansi said.

"I didn't know melons
could talk," said Elephant.

"Of course we do. We talk all the time.
The trouble is, you never listen."

"I can't believe my ears!" Elephant exclaimed.
"A talking melon! Who could believe it?
I must show this to the king."

75 🐝

Elephant ran down the road,

carrying the melon with Anansi inside.

Along the way, he ran into Hippo.

"Where are you going with that melon?" Hippo asked.

"I'm taking it to the king," Elephant told him.

"What for? The king has hundreds of melons."

"He doesn't have one like this," Elephant said.

"This is a talking melon."

Hippo didn't believe Elephant. "A talking melon?

What an idea! That's as ridiculous as . . ."

". . . a skinny hippo," the melon said.

Hippo got so angry his face turned red.

"Who said that? Did you say that, Elephant?"

"It wasn't me. It was the melon," Elephant said.
"I told you it talks. Do you believe me now?"

"I do!" Hippo exclaimed. "I want to go with you.
I want to hear what the king says
when you show him this talking melon."

"Come along, then," said Elephant.
So Elephant and Hippo went down the road together,
carrying the melon.

By and by, they ran into Warthog.
"Where are you taking that melon?"
Warthog asked them.

"We're taking it to the king,"
Elephant and Hippo told him.

"What for? The king has hundreds of melons,"
Warthog said.

"He doesn't have one like this," Hippo replied.
"This melon talks. I heard it."

Warthog started to laugh. "A talking melon?
Why, that's as ridiculous as . . ."

". . . a handsome warthog," said the melon.

Warthog got so angry he shook all over.

"Who said that? Did you say that, Elephant?
Did you say that, Hippo?"

"Of course not!" Hippo and Elephant told him.
"The melon talks. Do you believe us now?"

"I do!" cried Warthog. "Let me go with you.
I want to see what the king does
when you show him this talking melon."
So Warthog, Elephant, and Hippo went
down the road together, carrying the melon.

Along the way, they met
Ostrich, Rhino, and Turtle.
   They didn't believe
the melon could talk either
until they heard it
for themselves.
Then they wanted
to come along too.

The animals came before the king.

Elephant bowed low as he placed the melon at the king's feet.

The king looked down. "Why did you bring me a melon?" he asked Elephant. "I have hundreds of melons growing in my garden."

"You don't have one like this," Elephant said. "This melon talks."

"A talking melon? I don't believe it. Say something, Melon."

The king prodded the melon with his foot.

The melon said nothing.

"Melon," the king said in a slightly louder voice, "there is no reason to be shy. Say whatever you like. I only want to hear you talk."

83 🦋

The melon still said nothing. The king grew impatient.

"Melon, if you can talk, I want you to say something.
I command you to speak."

The melon did not make a sound.

The king gave up. "Oh, this is a stupid melon!" he said.

Just then the melon spoke. "Stupid, am I?
Why do you say that? I'm not the one
who talks to melons!"

The animals had never seen the king so angry.
"How dare this melon insult me!" he shouted.
The king picked up the melon and hurled it
as far as he could.

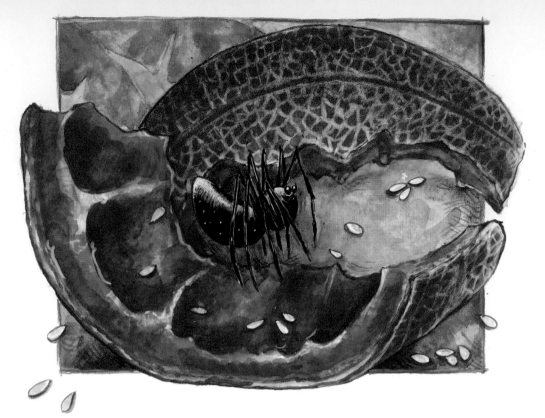

The melon bounced and rolled all the way

to Elephant's house. KPOM! It smacked into the thorn tree

and burst into pieces. Anansi picked himself up

from among the bits of melon rind.

　　All the excitement had made him thin.

And now that he was thin again,

he was hungry. Anansi climbed the banana tree.

He settled himself in the middle of a big bunch of bananas

and started eating.

Elephant returned. He went straight to the melon patch.

"You melons got me in trouble with the king!" Elephant said.

"From now on, you can talk all you like.

I'm not going to listen to a word you say!"

"Good for you, Elephant!" Anansi called from the bananas.

"We bananas should have warned you.

Talking melons are nothing but trouble."

Battle scene from the frontispiece to *Sinbad the Sailor*. 1923. Paul Klee.

Watercolor. Durst-Haase Collection, Muttenz. Photo: Giraudon/Art Resource

Peter and the Wolf. 1943. Ben Shahn.

Tempera. 6 1/2" x 10". Private collection. © 1994 Estate of Ben Shahn/VAGA, NY. Photo: SCALA/Art Resource

FINE ART
FOLK TALES

Bunraku performance in
Osaka, Japan.

Photo: Werner Forman Archive/Art Resource

The Sleeping Beauty from a series illustrating the *Legend of the Briar Rose*.
Series painted 1871–1890. Sir Edward Burne-Jones.

Oil on canvas, 61 x 82.5 cm. Faringdon Collection, Buscot, Oxfordshire, Great Britain. Photo: Bridgeman/Art Resource

THE LION AND THE MOUSE

Aesop

illustrated by Alexi Natchev

A large lion was napping in the shade
when a little mouse ran across his tummy.
This tickled the lion,
so he grabbed the little mouse.
The mouse squeaked with fear.

"Oh, please don't eat me," squeaked the mouse.
"I'm so small I wouldn't even make one good bite.
Let me go, and some day I could help you."

"Now that's funny!" roared the lion.
"How could a little thing like you
ever help me, the king of the jungle?"
But the lion let the mouse go.

Weeks and weeks went by.

One day the mouse heard the lion
roaring. The lion seemed to be in pain.

The mouse ran to the lion.
He had been caught by hunters.
His paws were tied with rope.

The mouse began to gnaw the rope
with his sharp little teeth.
He worked a long, long, time.
At last the lion was free!

The mouse said, "There, you see!
You'd be in big trouble if it weren't for me."

The grateful lion smiled. "So I see,
my little friend. So I see."

THE WOLF IN SHEEP'S CLOTHING

Aesop

illustrated by Normand Chartier

92

Once upon a time a hungry wolf saw some sheep in a pen. "If I could live in that pen, I would never have to hunt for my dinner again," said the wolf.

The wolf found an old sheep's skin. He put it over him and jumped into the pen.

Quick as a wink, the wolf grabbed a nice, fat sheep.

The shepherd saw what the wolf was doing. He raced over with a big stick in his hand.

"Stop!" he cried.

"Don't yell at me," said the wolf. "I'm just one of your sheep."

"No," said the shepherd. "You are a wolf."

"How do you know?" asked the wolf.

"You may be dressed like a sheep," said the shepherd, "but you act like a wolf."

Then the shepherd drove the wolf away.

THE THREE BILLY GOATS GRUFF

retold by Christine Crocker

illustrated by Cat Bowman Smith

Once upon a time there were
three billy goat brothers named Gruff.
The three billy goats lived by a river.
Across the river was a meadow with tall green grass.
One day, the billy goats
wanted to cross the river to eat the grass.
But there was only one bridge across the river.
And under that bridge lived a mean, hungry troll.
The troll had eyes as big as saucers
and a nose as long as a poker.

First the little billy goat Gruff started
across the bridge. His little feet went trip trap,
trip trap on the bridge.
The troll heard the noise.

"Who's that trip-trapping over my bridge?"
roared the troll.

"It is only I, the little billy goat Gruff,"
said the goat in his tiny voice.

"I'll eat you for my breakfast!"
said the troll.

"Oh, please don't," said the goat. "I'm much too small.
Wait until my big brother comes. He'd be a much better
breakfast for a big troll like you."

95

"Very well," said the greedy troll.

So he let the little billy goat Gruff cross the bridge.

Next, the middle-sized billy goat Gruff started across the bridge. His middle-sized feet went trip trap, trip trap.

"Who's that trip-trapping over my bridge?" shouted the troll.

"It's only I, the middle-sized billy goat Gruff,"
said the goat in his middle-sized voice.
"I'll eat you for my breakfast!" roared the troll.
And he jumped up on the bridge.
"Oh, please don't," said the goat.
"I'm much too small. Wait for my big brother.
He'd be a much better meal for a big troll like you."
"Very well," said the greedy troll.
So he let the middle-sized billy goat Gruff cross the bridge.

97

Soon the big billy goat Gruff started
across the bridge.
His big feet went trip trap, trip trap.
The bridge shook.

"**Who's that trip-trapping over my bridge?**"
shouted the troll.

"**It is I, the big billy goat Gruff!**"
said the goat in his big voice.

"I'll eat you for my breakfast!"
roared the troll.

"Oh no, you won't," said the goat. The big billy
goat Gruff ran at the troll and butted him into the river.
The troll was never heard of again.

99

Then the three billy goats Gruff went
into the meadow. They ate all the grass
they wanted and lived happily ever after.
And so—
Snip, snap, snout,
This tale's told out.

LITTLE GREEN RIDING HOOD

Gianni Rodari

illustrated by Nadine Bernard Westcott

Grandpa: Once upon a time there was a little girl called Little Yellow Riding Hood.

Child: No! Red Riding Hood!

Grandpa: Oh yes, of course, Red Riding Hood.

Well, one day her mother called and said:

"Little Green Riding Hood—"

Child: Red!

Grandpa: Sorry! Red.

"Now, my child, go to Aunt Mary
and take her these potatoes."

Child: No! It doesn't go like that!
         "Go to Grandma and take her
         these cakes."

Grandpa: All right.

So the little girl went off, and in the wood
she met a giraffe.

Child: What a mess you're making of it!
It was a wolf!

Grandpa: And the wolf said:

"What's six times eight?"

Child: No! No! The wolf asked her where

she was going.

Grandpa: So he did. And Little Black Riding Hood replied—

Child: Red! Red!! Red!!!

Grandpa: She replied: "I'm going to the market to buy some tomatoes."

Child: No she didn't. She said: "I'm going
to my Grandma, who is sick,
but I've lost my way."

Grandpa: Of course! And the horse said—

Child: What horse? It was a wolf.

Grandpa: So it was. And this is what it said:
"Take the 75 bus, get out
at the main square, turn right, and
at the first doorway you'll find three steps.
Leave the steps where they are, but
pick up the dime you'll find lying
on them, and buy yourself a packet
of chewing gum."

Child: Grandpa, you're terribly bad at
          telling stories. You get them all wrong,
          but all the same, I wouldn't mind
          some chewing gum.

Grandpa: All right here's your dime.
          Now I'll finish reading my newspaper.

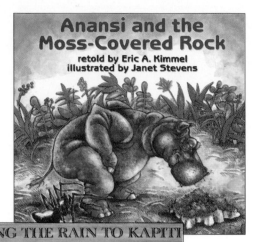

BIBLIOGRAPHY

Anansi and the Moss-Covered Rock

retold by Eric A. Kimmel

What happens when someone says,

"Isn't that a strange moss-covered rock"?

Bringing the Rain to Kapiti Plain

by Verna Aardema

Ki-pat finds a way to bring rain to "the

grass all brown and dead, that needed

the rain from the cloud overhead—"

Lon Po Po

by Ed Young

Three children are at home alone.

What will they do when the wolf comes?

The Monkey and the Crocodile

by Paul Galdone

A crocodile wants to catch a monkey,

but the monkey has ideas of his own.

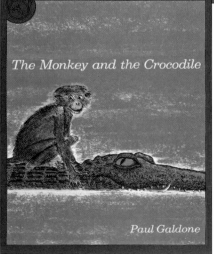

Moon Rope/Un lazo a la luna
by Lois Ehlert
Fox and Mole braid grass into a long rope so that they can climb to the moon. Mole slips and comes back to earth. Did Fox make it?

Nine-in-One, Grr! Grr!
told by Blia Xiong,
adapted by Cathy Spagnoli
Shao promises Tiger nine cubs each year. Bird thinks of a way to keep this from happening.

The Old Woman and Her Pig
adapted by Eric A. Kimmel
How will the old woman ever get her pig to go over the stile?

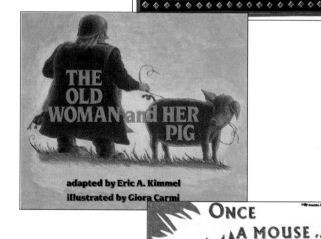

Once a Mouse . . .
by Marcia Brown
A hermit changes his pet mouse to a cat, to a dog, to a tiger, and back to a mouse again.